LAUGHTER
DAY SAINTS

by David Burnett

Cover art by David Burnett
Cover design copyrighted 2007 by Covenant Communications, Inc.
Published by Covenant Communications, Inc.
American Fork, Utah

Printed in Canada
First Printing: May 2007

12 11 10 09 08 07   10 9 8 7 6 5 4 3 2 1

ISBN 978-1-59811-313-6

LAUGHTER
DAY SAINTS

by David Burnett

"OK, Elder, perhaps your companion is young looking and maybe even a bit immature. That still doesn't change the fact that he's your senior companion."

Although Mervyn had enjoyed dancing with Helen most of the evening, he couldn't help worrying that once the lights came on he might not find her as attractive as he had hoped.

"We'd like to acknowledge our stake pie councilman
on the stand with us today."

Brother Cassidy and the Youth Dance Kid:
the fastest home teachers in the West.

After encouraging, pleading, and even bribing, the elders quorum presidency tried a new method of motivating delinquent home teachers.

"Oh great! You just had to go and mention
the Resurrection, didn't you?!"

The Las Vegas 18th Ward Elvis Inpersonator Choir

"Well, that certainly explains a lot."

"How many times do I have to tell you boys?
No scary masks in the building!"

After reaching the walls of Jerico,
Israel unleashes its secret weapon—Zebediah Gillespie.

"Oh, isn't that precious! Would sweet kitty like
to sit on the other nice elder's lap?"

After an accidental meeting at their orthodontist, it was love at first sight.
After that, Brad and Tiffany were never seen apart.

After years of waking everyone for church, leading the hymns,
and barndoor greeting, Russ was finally called
to be the new ranch president.

13

"A rather cliquish bunch, would't you say?"

Timmy and Igor had felt fairly confident that their science
merit badges were in the bag until the fateful moment
when Frankenscout broke free of his restraints.

"When I asked you eighteen months ago to wait for me,
I didn't mean here at the airport."

Always an innovator and usher extraordinaire,
Melvin tried a new tactic to help the high councilman
realize that he was way overtime on his talk.

"You guys really take the cake! Everyone knows that you never home teach the Millers on a full moon!"

"Oh my! I could really go for some spareribs right now!
How about you?"

". . . So there he was in his natural habitat, chewing on a cheese puff, when Elder Horton slips up behind 'im and then . . . kapow! Drops 'im like a bad habit."

After deciding to follow the bishop's advice on delegation,
Sister Weatherly chooses the perfect counselors.

"All right you guys, at the count of three,
we'll exchange prisoners. Remember . . . no funny stuff!"

"All who can support Brother Thurkel as our
ward employment specialist . . ."

Cultural Exchange

"Hey man, I hear they're lookin' for a new bishop.
I'm sweatin' it! How 'bout you?"

27

"The results are in, and it's even worse than we thought. Our entire ward choir is completely and utterly tone deaf."

29

"Oh great! Now we'll never get our books signed!"

"Hey dad! Our gnome teachers are here!"

After Mike had popped in a Mormon Tab CD
and checked his rearview mirror, he began to wonder
if dating the stake president's daughter was really worth the hassle.

As he sat and ate his cereal that morning, Elder Tanner suddenly had the impression that his new greenie would be an AP one day.

"He says if it was good enough for King Benjamin,
then it's good enough for him."

35

"He might not be much to look at, but he's
an RM with a good job so we're not complaining."

"I can't wait to see the look on Dad's face when he wakes up
and sees his new makeover!"

"Oh, ha ha ha! You guys are sooooooo funny!
I'd like to see you live without soap for two whole years!"

Every day for four long years, BYU–Idaho student
Theodore Wilkowski stood in front of the cafeteria's menu
and pondered what he should eat for lunch.

The Stake Low Council

Napoleon Dynamite II
After Kip locates a real time machine on eBay,
Napoleon and Pedro send Uncle Rico back to 1982.

John the Baptist—the dating years

Sister Jones would recall years later that Alma the Younger
and the sons of Mosiah started to go downhill about the
time they started sporting their new CTW rings.

45

Pioneer Wagster Race

Every year around Halloween, Bishop Brown couldn't resist
the old hand-in-the-candy-jar trick.

"Boys, you're looking at the most feared driver
on the Pinewood Derby Circuit."

"Oh sure, he's kinda quiet, and when you're tracting, ladies faint and stuff, but let me tell ya . . . the guy is one heck of a spiritual giant!"

"Well, I stand corrected!
Wild horses actually can drag Thurmon to church!"

Witnesses would later state on the accident report that
Lorretta knew perfectly well that it was Leonard's calling
to hold up the wall during singles dances.

With the unique ability to unlock her jaws and hit
a high C note at 400 decibels, Sister Johnson soon became
a legend among church ward choirs.

"So Mr. Moneybags is too good to wear hand-me-ups, is he now?"

That night at their annual Christmas party, the Physics Club members felt pretty foolish about their matchmaking endevors after realizing that Kevin and Shelia were too much alike to be attracted to each other.

"I guess I'd better have my hearing aid checked.
I thought for sure you said to set him apart as a high priest."

It didn't take Moses long to grow weary of
being mistaken for Charlton Heston.

"Five Thanksgiving dinners back to back!
I believe we just broke the mission record, Elder!"

Brother Whittenbeck—world-famous Sunday School truancy officer

"The new calling sounds great, Bishop, but I'm gonna have to clear it with my Space Cadet Club first!"

Every Sunday, Sister Thornburg struggled to keep her students
in class until their wives picked them up.

"Henry was going great guns on his mother's line
and then all of a sudden . . . Wham! He hit a brick wall."

J. Golden Kimball's secretary, Clara Milburn, was able to retire after only two years of service due to the success of her "Swear Jar."

"The good news is that the entire curriculum is in for next year. The bad news, however, is that it's entirely in Mandarin Chinese."

"I've got to admit, folks, that when Frank and I decided to make *Mormon Mayhem Basketball*, I said, 'Man, this is gonna be like shooting fish in a barrel!'"

Jacob Wrestles the Angel

"It's my companion, President! He's always trying
to put words in my mouth!"

"Boys, I'd like you to meet our new ward bouncer!"

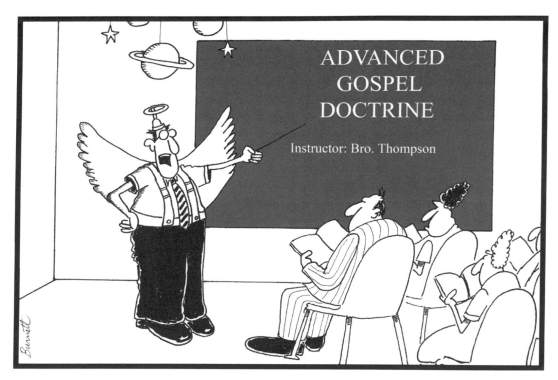

"I heard that blob-from-Kolob remark, Sister Gille!
Don't make me fly back there!"

"I really can't explain why I speed, President. I guess
I just have a heavy foot or something."

71

Ralph Gumbert enters his high priest quorum for the very first time,
excited at the opportunity for spiritual and intellectual growth.

73

"So first the bad news. We figure you froze on the way to class about twenty-six years ago, your girlfriend is probably a grandmother by now, and last . . . uh . . . well, you'd better brace yourself for what I'm about to show you."

Mormon Tab Boot Camp

Methuselah Takes His Family to the Fair

"It's impolite to stare at your food, Elder."

"Fantastic! Sister Burton lasted three minutes and twenty-one seconds!
Looks like we have a new nursery record, brethren."

Brother Harris would soon become the wealthiest member in his ward due to the frequent visits of the Hair Fairy.

"Just stopped in to see how your research was going,
but on second thought . . ."

"All right, folks! Let's speed it up! I haven't got all day, you know!"

"After going through the hymn book twice, Bishop,
I'm starting to suspect that 'Great Balls of Fire' isn't even in there."

"Oh, come on, Elder! With a name like 'Tiny,' how bad can he be?"

"Well, look what we have here! You must think Brother Bob and I don't take our door greeting assignments very seriously, Sister Myers."

One fateful evening, Elders Smith and Martinez discovered what their mission president actually did on his P-days.

"Don't worry, Mrs. Martin. We'll have your husband refitted with a lawn mower and back out in your yard in no time."

Rather dissatisfied with the nursery experience,
J. Morton Muttonberg had hoped that Sunbeams would
be a bit more intellectually challenging.

Of all the plagues of Egypt, the Eleventh Plague actually
proved to be the most horrible.

"You ever notice that the missionaries seem
to look younger every year?"

"Brother Brown said he didn't feel welcome when he moved in last month, so we decided to remedy the situation."

"I haven't missed a meeting in forty years,
and I don't plan to start now!"

"So the two of you decided to cut each other's hair
to save money. Brilliant!"

". . . and for the first time in ten years, Don gave up the Super Bowl to come to church! It's a miracle!"

Agnes couldn't help feeling that she would never quite fit
into the Stepford Ward Relief Society, despite their
best intentions and sunny dispositions.

"And it came to pass that I, Nephi, being exceeding young, nevertheless being large in stature . . ."

"Looks like our bishopric meeting is going to run over again, honey!"

"Wait a minute! He doesn't look alive to me! I want my money back!"

When the fellas needed a safe ride home, they could always depend on good ol' stone-cold-sober Chuck, a devout Moomon.

DAVID E. BURNETT grew up in the small town of Sanderson, Florida. As a child, he developed an interest in cartooning from the daily newspaper comics and also from watching Saturday morning cartoons. This in turn led to drawing cartoons in school when he should have been tending to his school work and even cartoons of his teachers, which, looking back, probably wasn't a good idea either. David and his wife, Cindy, have five children and are members of the Calhan Ward in Eastern Colorado.